THE SATURDAY EVENING POST CARTOON FESTIVAL

25 years of POST cartoons

THE SATURDAY EVENING POST

CARTOON

FESTIVAL

Selected by Marione R. Nickles

1958
E. P. Dutton & Co., Inc.
New York

FOREWORD

For the very young or the very forgetful, let's brush up a little on what was happening twenty-five years ago.

The Roosevelt family had just moved into the White House for what turned out to be a rather lengthy stay. We were deep in the depression and as we fought our way back to stability about the only thing we could afford was conversation. We talked about Russia and communism, jigsaw puzzles, IQ tests, books, and whose system was best for contract bridge. In those days before TV, we kept our radios turned on around the clock, played countless games of miniature golf and attended double features where you couldn't hear the dialogue for the rattle of free dishes. As the 30's merged with the 40's, we were concerned with more pressing anxieties—the situation in Europe and the Far East, the rumors of war and our involvement in it, our fast-growing two-ocean Navy, our preparedness program and the new peacetime conscription plan known as the Selective Service Act. And then, of course, Pearl Harbor.

During the next years, with our men fighting thousands of miles away, we battled the petty annoyances of the home front. We stood in line for hours to buy one pack of cigarettes (never mind what brand), a quarter of a pound of butter, a piece of honest-to-goodness beef. We struggled with the irritations of the ration books, the stickers for this, the coupons for that, and points, points, points for everything else. There was a shortage of household help, a shortage of doctors and dentists, paper, cars, rubber, gasoline, stockings. . . . and manpower. But we still had womanpower and the ladies—God bless them—stepped in. They joined the Armed Services. They laid down the skillet, the broom and the dustrag and picked up the riveting machine. They drove taxis and busses, worked in defense plants, on the railroads, on ships. And when it was all over, there were the rough days of adjustment for everyone.

Newspapers, magazines and books give us the facts, the statistics, the history. It is the cartoonists who possess a peculiar and wonderful talent. They give us the therapeutic gift of laughter. They hold our faults, failings and miseries up to the light, give them a slight twist and have us chuckling at ourselves before we know it. Their contribution to our daily life over the troubled years has been important, delightful and continuing.

There are close to three hundred and fifty cartoons in *The Saturday Evening Post Cartoon Festival*, taken from over thirty thousand published in the POST. In making the selection I deliberately chose those that clearly showed the interests of the day and yet, I thought, would be understandable to a wide audience. (I see no advantage to a joke that has to be studied and explained to be enjoyed.) They are arranged in sequence, rather than in arbitrary groupings, in the belief that continuity will itself best serve to point up the fads, foibles and follies that amused or worried us during the past quarter of a century.

The choice was not difficult to make in spite of the volume of material. Although you may see here a marked change in the manner of delivery or presentation and certainly of style among the well-known cartoonists of America, humor has no fixed point in time.

All I can hope is that you have half as much pleasure in reading this anthology as I had in putting it together.

MARIONE R. NICKLES

1933-1941

"Resisting an officer, Heh?"

HENRY

"Do we have to do whatever we want to again today?"

Get a horse!"

"Yes, Oeufs! Them's eggs in french!"

"We'll give her all six, and get the title back in the United States!"

"They're for keeping track of Mrs. Roosevelt!"

13

"Well, military school
was *your* idea!"

"Could we count on you, Miss Pringle,
in our drive for better babies?"

"It's about time the United States recognized us!"

"It's called 'the dove' and signifies peace!"

LITTLE LULU

"What do you say we go over and rag
Peabody about the Boston Tea Party."

"I feel I've lost my own personality—since
dem nice bulls showed us tru de bird cage."

17

"Well! That settles it. Next time I'm going to whirl around an' give him a dirty look!"

"JUNGLE LIFE" FILMED IN AFRICA

WORLD PREMIERE

John Rosol

"I wish you'd speak to mother. She's making baby things again!"

19

DRAWN BY GREGORY D'ALESSIO

"—I just dashed off this poem to you in
a free moment. I hope you'll like it."

"It's called 'Gone With the Wind.'
Shall I tell you about it?"

DRAWN BY SALO

"Oh, yes, I adore Walt Whitman. He deserves to be called the 'King of Jazz'."

"—and this is our bowling instructor!"

"I thought I'd NEVER get here!"

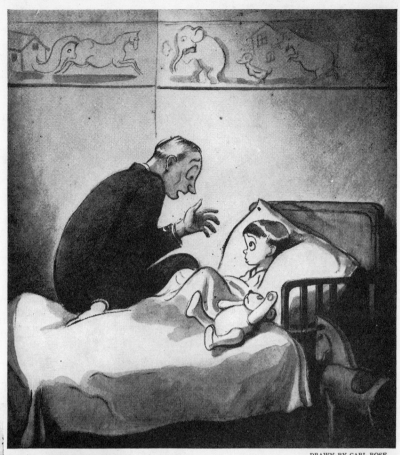

"It was exactly eight years ago this month. Billions in values were wiped out. There were paupers that afternoon who but a few hours earlier had been millionaires. Down, down, down went prices—suddenly the room was electrified, someone had shouted, '210 for 100,000 U. S. Steel Common—'"

23

"—Enclosed you will find twenty-five cents for an autographed photograph of Myrna Loy . . ."

"Papa's going to turn a page. Everybody ready?"

24

"Hello, Sergeant! They've won over my horse! They've won over my horse!"

"Hello, Ma! hello, Pa!"

"I'll drive your car through—I'm the new pilot here!"

"Now, it was butterflies you came out here to collect originally, wasn't it professor?"

"That's the Society Editor
transcribing his notes."

"We, the Jury, find the defendant guilty — don't we
boys?"

"*Now* may I have those letters back?"

"I am Brave Eagle. This my son, Fighting
Hawk, and my grandson, Martin Bomber."

"Tears, Miss La Rue, tears! Just imagine your bank failed! Your swimming pool leaks and your new $10,000 limousine burned up last night!"

"Starting tomorrow I'm boycotting Japan, so I don't
want to run out of silk stockings."

"This is my system for pushing through crowds."

"We get along fine—I like goat's milk
and she's crazy about rejection slips."

"That doesn't work either, Mother. Every time I start to
cry, *he* bursts into tears, and then where am I?"

"Well! What are you so happy about?"

"What was it Sherman said about Christmas?"

"Poor Winthrop! Europe's
got beyond him!"

"He just sits and mopes over that new Jefferson nickel!"

"Whoa, Nelly—down, Martha—howdy, Esther."

"Spencer Tracy, I presume?"

"You mean I'll even have to *look* at 'Oatsy-Woatsies'?"

"He's this kind of a fellow—his name is
Thomas and we *call* him Thomas."

"Well, do you want to go to a wretched dinner at those awful Mitchells'? I can't keep my hand over this mouthpiece all day!"

"This is a guest room. . . .
That's a guest."

LITTLE LULU

"Dad's going to *hate* my being kept back for a third term. He's Republican, you know."

"Nothing visible, sir, except a sleek white gull wheeling with lazy grace across the dark winter sky."

"Can I keep him, Mom?—
He followed me home."

"He offered to leave his brain
to science, but they wanted
time to think it over."

"Look, I can't get it off.
Isn't that silly!"

"You needn' chuckle and nod your head understandingly any longer, dear. The company went home fifteen minutes ago."

"Gentlemen, I bring you glad tidings—my wife has okayed our plans."

"The pens *still* don't write!"

41

"This yours?"

"And this is Miss Andrews,
our bottleneck."

"The back straight, Mrs. Quinn; heels down and slightly in; the arms loose at the sides, grasping the reins lightly between the thumb and first finger."

"His revenge was rather neat. He named a tugboat after her."

"It's gonna be nip and tuck this year, I guess."

"Cut the speech short—we wanta get started building the next ship."

"Your father and I have decided to treat you to a baby."

"Last year it was beetles."

"That isn't as easy as it looks."

"If I could live my life over again, I think I would have played that five no-trump different last night . . ."

"Do you get it, so far?"

"You might as well give up that notion. Nobody's going to dash in with a last-minute reprieve."

"Can't you miss The Lone Ranger just this once?"

"Have you spoken to the colonel yet about my suggestion for using paper plates?"

"I think I need defrosting."

49

"Tell Aunt Katie, grandpop, Sarah Lang and Cousin Phil, thanks for the copies of 'Dere Mabel.'"

"In case of war I understand the Government is going to call out the Federal Reserve."

"Joe sent me. I want five gallons of gas."

1942-1945

"Selective Service? Would you kindly select five or
six men to come to a birthday party next Thursday?"

"That's Professor Watkins—Current History."

"They haven't relaxed an instant since the morning of December seventh."

"Er—isn't there some *other* way to get to the diner?"

"That will be all, Mrs. Beal. Thank you *so* much."

CHAS. CARTWRIGHT

"Look, dear, I only *own* a defense factory—I don't work in one!"

"Why of course I love you . . . er . . . ah . . . er . . . ah . . . Geraldine!"

PRIVATE BREGER

"Private Breger's busy just now. Can you sing that birthday telegram later?"

"I think it was wonderful of you to
try and explain it to me!"

"Well before I make an ap-
pointment, I'd like to know
if there's any chance of *this*
doctor being called to the
Army before next March."

"SILENCE! H. V. Kaltenborn!"

"Isn't she feeling well, or
is it that Frank Sinatra?"

"I represent the Federal Man-power Commission. How are you fixed for help?"

"Sometimes a voice within me cries,
  'Oh, the futility of it all.' "

"Mr. Hobbs, we really feel that you deserve a sack."

"Of course, to follow my plan completely they'd have to bring everybody back to the United States and start all over."

"Don't say anything. I think they're just trying to attract our attention."

"What'll I do? They keep yelling, 'Put it on.'"

"Back home, by this time in the morning I'd have the stove a-goin', breakfast ate, fed the chickens and pigs and done all the milkin'."

"For some reason, your father seems to dislike me."

"Just tell her 'Old Blood and Guts' called."

"Now remember, Grandma doesn't approve of there being two sexes."

64

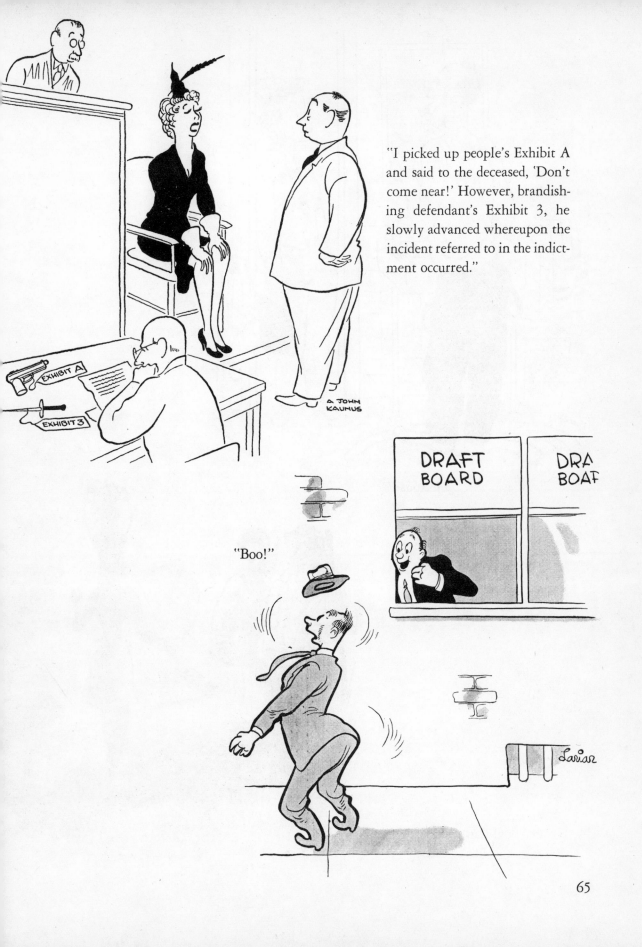

"I picked up people's Exhibit A and said to the deceased, 'Don't come near!' However, brandishing defendant's Exhibit 3, he slowly advanced whereupon the incident referred to in the indictment occurred."

"Boo!"

65

"Jealous?"

"Oh, boy! Can't you just picture her
in a sweater?"

"What shall I do, sir? This is the first time anything like this has happened in basic training."

1.

2.

3.

4.

"Are you hurt?"

"Since I got here the only person I've seen from home that
I knew was Roosevelt!"

"Do you suppose my working on an assembly line had anything to do with it?"

"When Bob Hope did this it was a scream."

"He explained to me that he's
with Army Intelligence."

"Anybody feel like shuffleboard?"

"There's a well-turned ankle."

"Needless to say, you're the first woman I've seen in six months."

"Helen! I've found where the new maid put the casserole!"

"Well, Mr. Strain—I see you stopped F.D.R.
in the middle of a speech again!"

"He blames it all on my mother; my dear mother, who
has lived with us from the day we were married and
who will be only too glad to testify that in all our
quarrels I was always in the right."

"I don't have no opinions on nothin'."

"It's nice to see everybody on the
same shift again."

THIS *AIN'T* THE ARMY

"If a man answers—hang on!"

"Good news, senator! I have a tax system figured out for next year that NOBODY will understand!"

"Points, points, points, points!"

"Either we've been robbed or daddy is home on a surprise furlough."

"I couldn't put it down. Matter of fact, I couldn't pick it up."

"Remember, I must have them Saturday, sure!"

"That sounds convincing to me.
How did the jury take it?"

"And now, Mr. Weathersby,
about that 1936 sedan you
were thinking of selling."

"Well, *look for it*—that's what I'd have to do!"

"Looking for someone?"

"And for giving up their regular time, Senator Smudge and this broadcasting company wish to thank Joe's wife, the Swing Quartet, Kiddies' Corner, the Zifties Hour, the Central Philharmonic, Quizz or Bizz, the Tune Parade, and Music for Sleeping."

"Why so polite all of a sudden—
been hearing peace rumors?"

JOHN
BAILEY

"Then in addition to being general man-
ager, there will be a few little 'extracur-
ricular' things for you to do!"

GEORGE RECKAS

82

Ted Key

"How's business?"

"I'd suggest you slow down and
take it easy."

"Aha! Just what I always suspected!"

"You know, I think he's got an idea there."

"After all, you're probably the nearest thing to a tourist
they've seen in three years!"

"Faster! Faster! Faster!"

"Let's suppose you want a large can of tomato juice. You don't just come piling in here and yell for it . . . but you bring what we call a ration book . . ."

"A man from Detroit gave the doctor the idea."

88

"If you don't like these, we have some other brands—Cornbelts, Golden Hay, Horses Neck, Sawdust Trail and Moochies."

"Oh, that's nothing! Wait until he gets a drink!"

"Did you miss me, Harvey?"

"Excuse the sneeze, old man—
catching cold, I guess! You say
there's a discrepancy in these gas
coupons?"

"I'll run along now, or you folks will
think I'm a regular old gossip."

BLAKLEY.

"Don't worry—I always pull
it off with one short shriek!"

91

"Mind if we sit the rest of this one out—my back's killing me."

Richter

THE LITTLE SCOUTS

"Did we pass our cooking test, Mr. Johnson?"

Roland Coe

"Watch his expression when he doesn't make it."

RIVETS

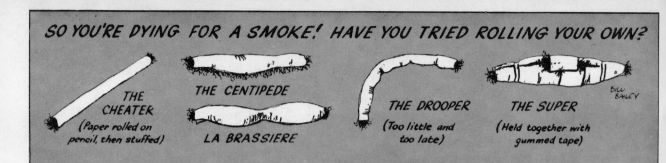

SO YOU'RE DYING FOR A SMOKE! HAVE YOU TRIED ROLLING YOUR OWN?

THE CHEATER
(Paper rolled on pencil, then stuffed)

THE CENTIPEDE

LA BRASSIERE

THE DROOPER
(Too little and too late)

THE SUPER
(Held together with gummed tape)

"He's doing nicely, thanks—takes an interest in food again and can read the papers. Of course, we still daren't mention a certain name."

1946-1952

"I was en promenade down the Champs Elysees,
and, alors, who should I run into but Myrtle.
'Ca va bien, Myrt?' I said. 'Betsy!' she screeched."

"Then my whole life seemed to pass before me—
all except the part where I had swimming lessons."

"I've never seen him smile."

"E above high C."

"I'm afraid I'm not very good company tonight."

"The major is having a
hard time converting to
a felt hat."

"Puts everything she's got into
that backstroke, doesn't she?"

"If you must whistle, Perkins, let's have something besides Stone Cold Dead in the Market for a change."

"Walter takes his fun where he finds it."

"Then we broke her of that two-o'clock feeding and put her on formula..."

"I spent my four years in the Army on a little island in the Pacific with nothing but a ping-pong table for amusement."

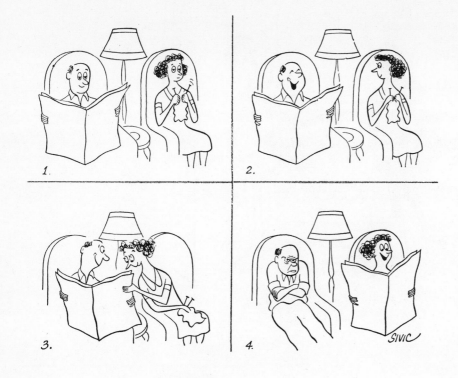

"I knew this was too good to last.
Byrd is on his way back."

"I hope you realize, madam, you'll have a lawsuit
on your hands if the kid lets go."

"Oh, heavens, no! I have to curl it
—it's straight as a stick!"

"In the middle of my sleep—BANG! I hear
jelly fall on a cracker."

"A man who doesn't know the
meaning of the word COM-
PROMISE; who doesn't know
the meaning of the word SUB-
MISSION; who doesn't know
the meaning of the word . . ."

"You've been in the mud again."

"Miss Leroy! Control yourself!"

"*Now* what do you want?"

"Then, without warning, my motor died—and he heard
what I was calling him."

"Perhaps you had better start with
the parallel bars."

"And now, gentlemen, no-
tice what happens when I
add potassium permanga-
nate."

dave gerard

"—It was nice visiting you two again. We've laughed about George having to sleep in the attic — and the bed falling in on him. Charlie says, tell George he'll return the $25.00 and the raincoat he took by mistake—."

"Better loosen your chin strap a little if you're gonna sit and yawn all evening."

TOM HENDERSON

"You have doubtless been asking yourselves, 'What is the nature of coal-tar derivatives?' That is what I am here to tell you."

"I want to burn with a hard, gemlike flame—to live, love, fight, succeed — and then I think — ah, the hell with it."

"Leftovers from what?"

"I'm afraid you're in trouble—they've shifted the emphasis again."

"If that's the best man, this is *really* a sorry affair."

"Uncle Squeely says that Cousin Coon, Auntie Possum, and Brother Bullfrog had a meeting and decided that you should go back ten hops and miss your next turn."

RIVETS

"She doesn't suspect a thing! She
thinks I forgot her birthday!"

"The market opened rather
irregular this morning."

". . . and we're setting the date as soon as Fred proposes."

"You were saying?"

"Everybody hang on real
tight in case he starts with
a sudden jerk!"

"I was in the neighborhood
and thought I'd come home."

M.Blanchard

"Yes, I said something.
I said, 'Ho-hum.' "

"Now you understand—you're not
being laid off. You're being fired
completely."

"He forgot that part about how we'll all end up in the poorhouse."

"...79, 80, 81, 82,..."   "1, 2, 3, 4..."

"Let's all stand now, and murder Hymn 147..."

"Look, let's put everything down and start all over again."

"Well, I found the perfect husband. Now I'm looking for a man just like him who is single."

"I found ten dollars today, in the tip of your old shoes, back in the corner of the hall closet, covered with your work pants."

"It's all fixed. His pants fall down in the second round."

"Boy, did SHE put up a fight!"

"I don't usually cry at weddings, but this one happens to be my own."

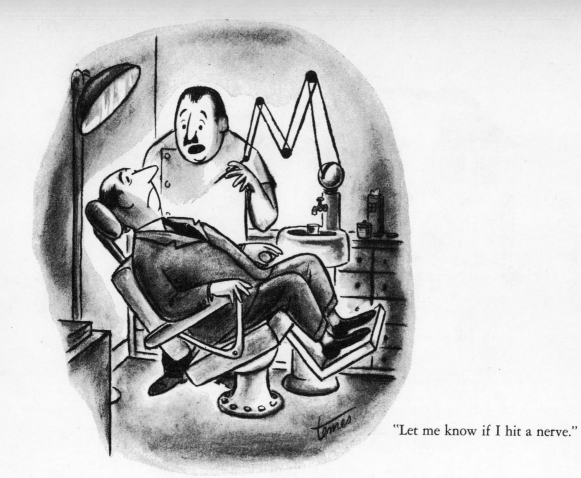

"Let me know if I hit a nerve."

"Oh, we get along swell . . . .
he hasn't moved from my side
all afternoon!"

"Nobody can cook like Mabel, but they came pretty close to it when I was in the army."

FAMOUS LAST WORDS...

"Oh, just wear anything. Nobody's bothering to dress."

"There's no rush on this, Hendricks—
take all night if necessary."

"We sail Monday or Tuesday,
depending on how fast they
unload the bananas."

"Allow me!"

"For a moment I thought it was your mother."

"THE KEYS! THE KEYS!
YOU'VE GOT THE KEYS
TO THE CAR . . ."

"...er...Dasher...Prancer...
Donner..."

"Now, there's no use arguing, Harry
—you're staying here tonight."

"If you can't discuss this thing in a calm, sensible, objective manner then I, for one, see no point in discussing it!"

1953-1957

"Well, we lost Esther!"

"The drain just said, 'Don't you dare turn on that faucet!'"

"I see where your secretary is carrying on an affair with her boss . . ."

"If you ask me, that's the way Prelude in C Sharp Minor should be played."

"Let me tell you what happened between John and Helen. . . . It's a scream."

"Seriously though — and in decent language—isn't that called a backlash?"

"Well, I'm sorry if I've incurred your displeasure!"

"He's going through a phase."

"Drove all the way from
El Paso—650 miles."

"Mind if I use the car myself tonight?
I'm taking your mother out tonight
and I want to impress her."

DRAWN BY GEORGE WOLFE

137

"Well, I guess I'd better be going."

"FRED!...FRED!...FRED!..."

"What's the topic?"

"I'm glad we had this little talk, mother—some of your ideas were pretty old-fashioned."

139

"Welcome to P.T.A. parents' night!"

"Could you try to relax a little
more, Mr. Forster?"

"It's a real cute toy. When he pull it, the wheels ring, the drum beats, the cymbals clang, and the horn plays 'Yankee Doodle.'"

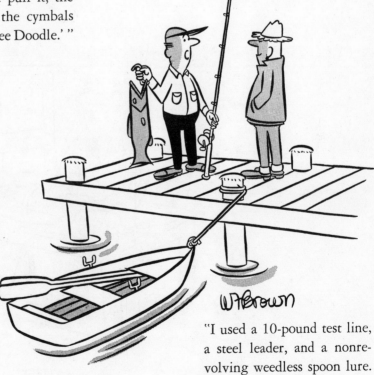

"I used a 10-pound test line, a steel leader, and a nonre-volving weedless spoon lure. Then when he got near the boat I hit him on the head with an oar."

"Suppose the crow had to walk and
carry a two-gallon gasoline can."

"Now, Hubble — what's
this nonsense about a
raise?"

"The next number is for Red and Skinny and from all the girls at the greasy spoon; to 'Bashful' from 'Blondie'; and from Keith Wilson from 'one who cares.'"

"... I would like to discuss your daughter's hand ... AHEM ... SIR, I would like to ..."

"This is a STACKUP?
. . . No . . . SLICKUP?
. . . No . . . Golly, you've
got a terrible handwrit-
ing!"

"Does this mean we don't
get any dessert?"

144

"Culminating a two year, billion dollar research program the United States today launched a man-made earth satellite about the size of a basketball . . ."

"James Cantwell . . . Cantwell Construction Company. Dear Sweater . . ."

"Step down, please."

"Why, I'll be happy to give you a tow. One minute while I get a piece of string."

"Our next speaker needs no introduction, because you wouldn't know him even if I told you who he is . . ."

"Let's not spoil it by figuring out what the same thing would cost at home."

"Greetings, Earthlings . . ."

"Do you have to *tell* everyone you're a Democrat and create those awful silences?"

"They're playing *Guy Lombardo!*
The wheel has come full circle!"

"Queen of spades!"

"But first a word
from our sponsor."

"Hello."

"Now back to
the show."

"Same as the last three times—the bees make honey and the birds lay eggs, and then he fades off to fill that pipe of his."

"...heaven forbid, of course."

"I hate child prodigies!"

"Harry feels he's reached
an absolute peak in high
fidelity."

SYVERSON

"We own 9,372 pieces of coal."

"What d'y' mean I'm not *happy?*
I'm happy as a lark!"

"That's my potato salad you're eating."

"Here it is . . . S-E-X."

"Parker, early morning
is no time for levity."

"May I ask *where* you studied engineering?"

"May I have a word with you?"

"Perhaps we'd better take him off that banana diet!"

"Gentlemen, Professor Diplip has some disturbing news about the new miracle vitamin X!"

"I try to take an interest in everything George does."

"... then we pinned the tail on the donkey ... then we ate ... then we played tag ... then I threw up ... then we all went home."

"What makes you think it's
a forgery?"

"I think he's the sweetest, hand-
somest, most intelligent man in
the whole world, and so does he."

"Just recite the poem, Mercedes . . . don't ham it up."

"By golly, you're right. There is a table back there!"

"No, you may not borrow my knife!"

"If you're through scrubbing that hand—
I'll need it to scrub my teeth."

"It takes a while to get the hang of it, Sam."

"... since there's
nothing new here
I'll close, Love,
Mother."

"Can those of you in the rear hear me clearly?"

"Speaking of stewed tomatoes, what time did the bridge club break up?"

"This is going to ruin my salt-free diet."

"Be down in a minute—I'm putting on my figure."

"Notice it has the same smooth, sleek fit in the back, also."

"I didn't say he chewed all forms of tobacco—I said he eschewed all forms of tobacco!"

"I may not get your entire
superstructure in this."

"We're waiting for you in surgery!"

"I found it."

"Did you ever get the feeling you haven't actually been to church?"

"Why on earth did you request Melancholy Baby?"

"Down, Fang!!"

"Still on liquids?"

"I suppose this was inevitable!"

171

"You realize, of course, you can't stay here tonight."

"This should be interesting."

"Quick, Norton . . . the gratitude switch."

"The prime coat dry yet?"

"Stop somewhere and put some more coffee into him—
his toast is in his pocket."

"Mr. Harcourt kidded me a little bit about some of my inadequacies today, so then I kidded *him* a little bit about some of *his*. But then, I don't know, the fun seemed to go out of it somehow."

"I didn't mean to pry. I just opened my letters without thinking."

". . . it's all right . . . he's just waiting for my other two wishes."

"... Now, after your mother threw the gravy in your
father's face, what happened?"

"How well did you say you
knew these woods?"

"Let's have another peek at that address."

"I'm worried."

"It's good to hear *your* voice
too! Who are you?"

"...as a matter of fact, you're even on the wrong railroad."

"Her 'something borrowed' is my boy friend."

"Watch, now . . . here comes the part I was telling
you about."

"... being of sound ... Alll aboooard ... mind and body ..."

"He wants that hamburger edible, whatever that means."

"Going to throw out the first arm of the season?"

"Oh, don't be such a prude! This may mean a big order for us!"

"Now, that's what I call a spring chicken."

"May I cut in?"

"Well, here it is the first of the month again."

"I just put that forkful in my ear."

"I know a small, out-of-the-way place where we could get a delicious dinner—it's called 'mother's.'"

"Now then . . . where does the hurt chest you?"

"None for me, thank you . . . it makes me cry."

"I lose more customers that way!"

"I couldn't sleep, so I thought I'd get some practicing
out of the way."

"Now dear, just relax."

"Yes, I notice something different . . . you've gone off your rocker."

"I'm washing a worm."

"We decided to walk to Sunday School."

"What seems to be the trouble, operator? I don't have all day, you know."